S0-AWT-940

GET READY for SCHOOL!

Music CD Includes **20** SONGS

GET READY FOR SCHOOL!

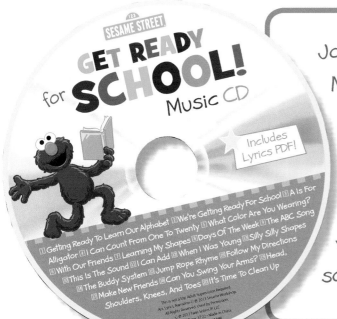

Join the parade and SING ALONG with Elmo, Cookie Monster, Big Bird, and the rest of your favorite *Sesame Street* friends as they get ready for school! From learning the alphabet to counting to 20, important skills are taught through sing-along songs. Extend the learning with the music CD and listen to upbeat, positive songs while at home or in the car!

 SING-ALONGS:

1. Getting Ready To Learn Our Alphabet
2. We're Getting Ready For School
3. A Is For Alligator
4. I Can Count From One To Twenty
5. What Color Are You Wearing?
6. With Our Friends

 BONUS TRACKS:

7. Learning Our Shapes
8. Days Of The Week
9. The ABC Song
10. This Is The Sound
11. I Can Add
12. When I Was Young
13. Silly Silly Shapes
14. The Buddy System
15. Jump Rope Rhyme
16. Follow My Directions
17. Make New Friends
18. Can You Swing Your Arms?
19. Head, Shoulders, Knees, and Toes
20. It's Time To Clean Up

We're gettin' ready to learn our **ALPHABET**
with our friends and we can't wait.
We're gettin' ready to learn our **ALPHABET**,
and it's gonna be just great.

We'll learn 26 letters and—soon you'll see—
We'll start with **A** and end with **Z**.
Zoe and Prairie Dawn will show us how.
We're ready to start right now.

We're gettin' ready to learn our **ALPHABET**
with our friends and we can't wait.
We're gettin' ready to learn our **ALPHABET**,
and it's gonna be just great.

Let's practice!

A B C D E F G H I J K L M N O P Q R S T U V W X Y Z

We're **GETTIN' READY**, we're **GETTIN' READY**
With our friends and we can't wait!
We're **GETTIN' READY** for school on Sesame Street,
And it's gonna be just great!

SCHOOL
BUS
STOP

Come on Big Bird show us the way.
There's a lot to learn—let's start **TODAY**!

ELMO, ZOE, and GROVER, too—
Are ready to learn with you!

We're **GETTIN' READY**,
We're **GETTIN' READY**,
With our friends and we can't wait!
We're **GETTIN' READY** for school
on Sesame Street
And it's gonna be just great!

We're learning **NUMBERS** and the **ALPHABET**
and the first day of school hasn't started yet.

Let's read together and sing a song.
Come on and sing along!

We're GETTIN' READY,
We're **GETTIN' READY**,
With our friends and we can't wait!
We're **GETTIN' READY** for school
on Sesame Street
And it's gonna be just great!

A is for **ALLIGATOR**.

B is for **BALL**.

C is for **CATERPILLAR**.

D is for **DOLL**.

E is for **ELEPHANT**.

F is for **FROG**.

G is for **GOAT**.

H is for **HOG**.

I is for **IGLOO**.

J is for **JAM**.

K is for **KITTENS**.

L is for **LAMB**.

M is for **MITTENS**.

N is for **NAIL**.

O is for **OCTOPUS**.

P is for **PAIL**.

 **Q** is for **QUARTER**.

12 MILES TO SESAME ST.

 is for **ROAD**.

S is for **SAILBOAT**.

T is for **TOAD**.

U is for **UMBRELLA**.

V is for **VINE**.

W is for **WORMS** who wiggle all the time.

X is for **X-ray**.

Y is for **YES**.

Z is for **ZOO**.
We're through, I guess.

I can count from ONE to TWENTY.
Listen, please! Listen, please!

1, 2, 3, 4, 5, 6, 7, 8, 9, 10, 11, 12! 11, 12!

I'll keep going. I'll keep going,
Higher up, higher up!

13, 14, 15, 16, 17, 18, 19, 20! 19, 20!

I can count from ONE to TWENTY.
Listen, please! Listen, please!

1, 2, 3, 4, 5, 6, 7, 8, 9, 10, 11, 12! 11, 12!

I'll keep going. I'll keep going,
Higher up, higher up!

13, 14, 15, 16, 17, 18, 19, 20! 19, 20!

1, 2, 3, 4, 5, 6, 7, 8, 9, 10, 11,
12, 13, 14, 15, 16, 17, 18, 19, 20!

If you are wearing **BLUE**, raise your hand.
If you are wearing blue, raise your hand.
If you are wearing blue, if you are wearing blue,
If you are wearing blue, raise your hand.

If you are wearing **RED**, stand up tall.
If you are wearing red, stand up tall.
If you are wearing red,
if you are wearing red,
If you are wearing red, stand up tall.

Elmo likes the color RED!
What's YOUR favorite color?

If you are wearing **GREEN**, march in place.
If you are wearing green, march in place.
If you are wearing green, if you are wearing green,
If you are wearing green, march in place.

If you are wearing **ORANGE**, touch your toes.
If you are wearing orange, touch your toes.
If you are wearing orange, if you are wearing orange,
If you are wearing orange, touch your toes.

If you are wearing **BLACK**,
start jumping jacks.
If you are wearing black, start jumping jacks.
If you are wearing black, if you are wearing black,
If you are wearing black, start jumping jacks.

With our friends we **LEARN** in school,
learn in school, learn in school.
With our friends we learn in school.
We all love to learn.

With our friends we **LAUGH** in school,
laugh in school, laugh in school.
With our friends we laugh in school.
We all love to laugh.

With our friends we **SING** in school,
sing in school, sing in school.
With our friends we sing in school.
We all love to sing.

After school we say **GOODBYE**,
say goodbye, say goodbye.
After school we say goodbye.
How do you say goodbye?

SO LONG, ADIOS, CIAO, ZAI JIAN...

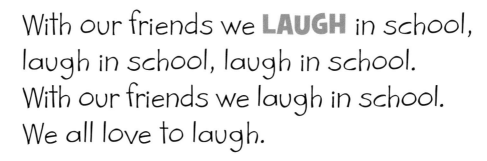

Music CD Includes **20 SONGS**

NURSERY RHYMES
with ELMO

NURSERY RHYMES WITH ELMO

SING ALONG with Elmo and his friends as they help put Humpty Dumpty back together again, get the Old Woman in the Shoe's children to go to sleep, and lead Mary's lamb out of school in this clever book featuring best-loved nursery rhymes. Extend the fun and learning with the music CD and listen to positive songs while at home or in the car!

 SING-ALONGS:

1. Oh Where, Oh Where Has My Little Dog Gone?
2. Humpty Dumpty
3. Little Boy Blue
4. Little Bo Peep
5. Twinkle, Twinkle Little Star
6. Hickory Dickory Dock
7. ABC Nursery Rhyme Game
8. The Old Woman Who Lived In A Shoe
9. This Old Man

 BONUS TRACKS:

10. Hey, Diddle Diddle
11. Wiggle, Giggle
12. Monster Munch
13. London Bridge
14. Mary Had A Little Lamb
15. Baa, Baa Black Sheep
16. This Little Pig
17. Jack And Jill
18. Pat-a-cake, Pat-a-cake
19. Little Miss Muffet
20. Wee Willie Winkie

Oh where, oh where has my **LITTLE DOG** gone?

Oh where, oh where can he be?

With his ears cut **SHORT** and his tail cut **LONG**,

oh where, oh where can he be?

HUMPTY DUMPTY sat on a wall.
HUMPTY DUMPTY had a great fall.
All the king's horses and all the king's men
couldn't put **HUMPTY** together again.

So some children came along
singing **HUMPTY'S** little song.
So they decided to think of a plan
to put **HUMPTY** together again.

Working with some glue and tape, they gave **HUMPTY** a new shape.
Now **HUMPTY DUMPTY** sits on a wall.
Never again will **HUMPTY** fall.

Now when **HUMPTY'S** story is told
a happy ending will unfold.
Working together to help **HUMPTY** mend!
Working together, they helped a friend!

LITTLE BOY BLUE

LITTLE BOY BLUE come blow your horn.

The sheep's in the meadow.

The cow's in the corn.

Where is the boy

who looks after the sheep?

He's under a haystack fast asleep.

LITTLE BO PEEP has lost her sheep and doesn't know where to find them. Leave them alone and they'll come home, wagging their tails behind them.

TWINKLE, TWINKLE, little star,
how I wonder what you are.

Up above the world so high, like a diamond in the sky.
TWINKLE, **TWINKLE**, little star, how I wonder what you are.

In the dark blue sky you keep, often through my curtains peep,

for you never shut your eye, till the sun is in the sky!

TWINKLE, **TWINKLE**, little star,
how I wonder what you are.

Hickory dickory dock!
The mouse ran up the clock.
The clock struck **ONE**.
The mouse ran down.
Hickory dickory dock!

Hickory dickory dock!
The mouse ran up the clock.
The clock struck **TWO**.
And down he flew.
Hickory dickory dock!

Hickory dickory dock!
The mouse ran up the clock.
The clock struck **THREE**.
The mouse said, "Watch me."
Hickory dickory dock!

Hickory dickory dock!
The mouse ran up the clock.
The clock struck FOUR.
The mouse said, "Once more."
Hickory dickory dock!

Hickory dickory dock!
The mouse ran up the clock.
The clock struck FIVE.
The mouse survived.
Hickory dickory dock!

A, B, C, D, E, F, G, H, I, J, K, L, M,
N, O, P, Q, R, S, T, U, V, W, X, Y, Z

Mary had a little lamb.
Its fleece was white as snow,
and everywhere that Mary went
the lamb was sure to go.

A, B, C, D, E, F, G, H, I, J, K, L, M,
N, O, P, Q, R, S, T, U, V, W, X, Y, Z

Little Bo Peep has lost her sheep
and can't tell where to find them.
Leave them alone and they'll come home,
wagging their tails behind them.

A, B, C, D, E, F, G, H, I, J, K, L, M,
N, O, P, Q, R, S, T, U, V, W, X, Y, Z

A, B, C, D, E, F, G, H, I, J, K, L, M,
N, O, P, Q, R, S, T, U, V, W, X, Y, Z

Humpty Dumpty sat on a wall.
Humpty Dumpty had a great fall.
All the king's horses and all the king's men
couldn't put Humpty together again.

A, B, C, D, E, F, G, H, I, J, K, L, M,
N, O, P, Q, R, S, T, U, V, W, X, Y, Z

Little Miss Muffet sat on a tuffet
eating her curds and whey.
Along came a spider and sat down beside her
and frightened Miss Muffet away.

A, B, C, D, E, F, G, H, I, J, K, L, M,
N, O, P, Q, R, S, T, U, V, W, X, Y, Z

THE OLD WOMAN WHO LIVED IN A SHOE

There was an old woman
who lived in a shoe,
she had so many children,
she didn't know what to do.

She gave them some broth
and a piece of bread,
and kissed them all gently,
and put them to bed.

This old man, he played **ONE**.
He played knick knack on my thumb.
With a knick knack paddy whack give a dog a bone,
This old man came rolling home.

This old man, he played **TWO**.
He played knick knack on my shoe.
With a knick knack paddy whack give a dog a bone,
This old man came rolling home.

This old man, he played **THREE**.
He played knick knack on my knee.
With a knick knack paddy whack give a dog a bone,
This old man came rolling home.

This old man, he played **FOUR**.
He played knick knack on my door.
With a knick knack paddy whack give a dog a bone,
This old man came rolling home.

This old man, he played **FIVE**.
He played knick knack on my hive.
With a knick knack paddy whack give a dog a bone,
This old man came rolling home.

This old man, he played **SIX**.
He played knick knack on my sticks.
With a knick knack paddy whack give a dog a bone,
This old man came rolling home.

This old man, he played **SEVEN**.
He played knick knack up in heaven.
With a knick knack paddy whack give a dog a bone,
This old man came rolling home.

This old man, he played **EIGHT**.
He played knick knack on my gate.
With a knick knack paddy whack give a dog a bone,
This old man came rolling home.

This old man, he played **NINE**.
He played knick knack on my spine.
With a knick knack paddy whack give a dog a bone,
This old man came rolling home.

This old man, he played **TEN**.
He played knick knack once again.
With a knick knack paddy whack give a dog a bone,
This old man came rolling home.

ELMO'S FAVORITE SONGS

Join the musical extravaganza and SING ALONG with Elmo, Cookie Monster, Big Bird, and the rest of your favorite *Sesame Street* friends as they practice counting in "Ten Little Bumblebees," and learn the importance of saying "please" and "thank you." Extend the fun and learning with the music CD and listen to upbeat positive songs while at home or in the car!

⭐ **SING-ALONGS:**

1. We're Getting Ready To Count
2. Ten Little Bumblebees
3. If You're Happy And You Know It
4. The Wheels On The Bus
5. Old MacDonald Had A Farm
6. Say "Please" And "Thank You"
7. Let Everyone Clap Hands
8. Alphabet Rock
9. The More We Sing Together

⭐ **BONUS SONGS:**

10. What Did Elmo Say?
11. Sing, Sing, Sing With Me
12. Ten In The Bed
13. There's No One Like Me
14. It's Silly Time
15. Row, Row, Row Your Boat
16. Down By The Bay
17. The Muffin Man
18. Playmate
19. Sally The Camel
20. Five Little Monkeys Jumping On The Bed

We're getting ready to **COUNT** on Sesame Street
with our friends and we can't wait.
We're getting ready to **COUNT** on Sesame Street
and it's gonna be just great.

We'll start at 1 and end with 10.
We'll really know our numbers then.
The Count is going to show us how.
We're ready to start right now.

We're getting ready to **COUNT** on Sesame Street
with our friends and we can't wait.
We're getting ready to **COUNT** on Sesame Street
and it's gonna be just great.

ONE little, **TWO** little, **THREE** little bumblebees;
FOUR little, **FIVE** little, **SIX** little bumblebees;
SEVEN little, **EIGHT** little, **NINE** little bumblebees;
TEN little bumblebees buzzing all around.

ONE little, **TWO** little, **THREE** little bumblebees;
FOUR little, **FIVE** little, **SIX** little bumblebees;
SEVEN little, **EIGHT** little, **NINE** little bumblebees;
TEN little bumblebees buzzing all around.

1, 2, 3, 4, 5, 6, 7, 8, 9, 10

TEN little bumblebees buzzing all around!

IF YOU'RE HAPPY AND YOU KNOW IT

If you're happy and you know it, **CLAP** your hands.
If you're happy and you know it, **CLAP** your hands.
If you're happy and you know it
then your face will surely show it.
If you're happy and you know it, **CLAP** your hands.

If you're happy and you know it, **STOMP** your feet.
If you're happy and you know it, **STOMP** your feet.
If you're happy and you know it
then your face will surely show it.
If you're happy and you know it, **STOMP** your feet.

If you're happy and you know it, shout **HOORAY**.
If you're happy and you know it, shout **HOORAY**.
If you're happy and you know it
then your face will surely show it.
If you're happy and you know it, shout **HOORAY**.

If you're happy and you know it, do **ALL THREE**.
If you're happy and you know it, do **ALL THREE**.
If you're happy and you know it
then your face will surely show it.
If you're happy and you know it, do **ALL THREE**.

The wheels on the bus go 'ROUND and 'ROUND,
'round and 'round, 'round and 'round.
The wheels on the bus go 'round and 'round,
all through the town.

BEEP
BEEP

SESAME STREET SCHOOL BUS

How do you get to school each day?

The people on the bus go **UP** and **DOWN**,
up and down, up and down.
The people on the bus go up and down,
all through the town.

The horn on the bus goes **BEEP, BEEP, BEEP**,
beep, beep, beep, beep, beep, beep.
The horn on the bus goes beep, beep, beep,
all through the town.

The wiper on the bus goes **SWISH, SWISH, SWISH**,
swish, swish, swish, swish, swish, swish.
The wiper on the bus goes swish, swish, swish,
all through the town.

The driver on the bus says, "**MOVE ON BACK**,
move on back, move on back."
The driver on the bus says, "Move on back,"
all through the town.

Old MacDonald had a farm, **E-I-E-I-O**.
And on that farm he had a cow, **E-I-E-I-O**.
With a moo moo here and a moo moo there.
Here a moo, there a moo, everywhere a moo moo.
Old MacDonald had a farm, **E-I-E-I-O**.

Old MacDonald had a farm, **E-I-E-I-O**.
And on that farm he had a pig, **E-I-E-I-O**.
With an oink oink here and an oink oink there.
Here an oink, there an oink, everywhere an oink oink.
Old MacDonald had a farm, **E-I-E-I-O**.

Old MacDonald had a farm, E-I-E-I-O.
And on that farm he had a horse, E-I-E-I-O.
With a neigh neigh here and a neigh neigh there.
Here a neigh, there a neigh, everywhere a neigh neigh.
Old MacDonald had a farm, E-I-E-I-O.

Old MacDonald had a farm, E-I-E-I-O.
And on that farm he had a dog, E-I-E-I-O.
With a ruff ruff here and a ruff ruff there.
Here a ruff, there a ruff, everywhere a ruff ruff.
Old MacDonald had a farm, E-I-E-I-O.

Old MacDonald had a farm, **E-I-E-I-O**.
And on that farm he had a cat, **E-I-E-I-O**.
With a meow meow here and a meow meow there.
Here a meow, there a meow, everywhere a meow meow.
Old MacDonald had a farm, **E-I-E-I-O**.

Old MacDonald had a farm, E-I-E-I-O.
And on that farm he had a duck, E-I-E-I-O.
With a quack quack here and a quack quack there.
Here a quack, there a quack, everywhere a quack quack.
Old MacDonald had a farm, E-I-E-I-O.

Nice to meet you!

Say "**PLEASE**" and "**THANK YOU**."
These are words that you need to know.
Say "**PLEASE**" and "**THANK YOU**."
These are words that you won't outgrow.
Say "**PLEASE**" and "**THANK YOU**."
Be polite and you will see that manners
are important to remember, yes indeed.

Say "It was nice to meet you"
or "Can I help you today?"
Say words that show kindness
and use them everyday.
Say "How are you doing?"
or "Please pass the yummy treats."
Say "Thank you for the present"
because manners can't be beat.

Say "**PLEASE**" and "**THANK YOU**."
These are words that you need to know.
Say "**PLEASE**" and "**THANK YOU**."
These are words that you won't outgrow.
Say "**PLEASE**" and "**THANK YOU**."
Be polite and you will see that manners
are important to remember, yes indeed.

Let everyone **CLAP HANDS** like me.
Let everyone **CLAP HANDS** like me.
Come on and join into the game.
You'll find that it's always the same.

Let everyone **LAUGH** like me.
Let everyone **LAUGH** like me.
Come on and join into the game.
You'll find that it's always the same.

Let everyone **CRY** like me.
Let everyone **CRY** like me.
Come on and join into the game.
You'll find that it's always the same.

Let everyone **SNEEZE** like me.
Let everyone **SNEEZE** like me.
Come on and join into the game.
You'll find that it's always the same.

Let everyone **WHISTLE** like me.
Let everyone **WHISTLE** like me.
Come on and join into the game.
You'll find that it's always the same.

A B C D E F G H I J K L M
N O P Q R S T U V W X Y Z

Now let's sing it again.

A B C D E F G H I J K L M
N O P Q R S T U V W X Y Z

That's the alphabet rock.

A B C D E F G H I J K L M N O P Q R S T U V W X Y Z

That's the alphabet rock.
That's the alphabet rock.
That's the alphabet rock.

THE MORE WE SING TOGETHER

The more we sing **TOGETHER**, together, together,
the more we sing **TOGETHER**, the happier we'll be.
For your friends are my friends
and my friends are your friends.
The more we sing **TOGETHER**, the happier we'll be!

ELMO & FRIENDS AT THE FARM

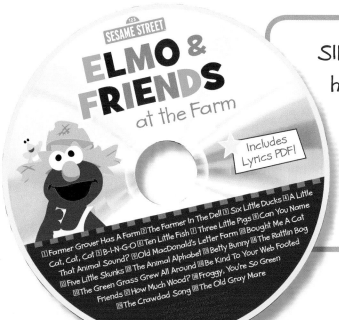

SING ALONG with Farmer Grover as he works on his farm. Count the six little ducks and laugh and learn about rhyming words in "A Little Cat, Cat, Cat." Extend the fun and learning with the music CD and listen to upbeat positive songs while at home or in the car!

SING-ALONGS:

1. Farmer Grover Has A Farm
2. The Farmer In The Dell
3. Six Little Ducks
4. A Little Cat, Cat, Cat
5. B-I-N-G-O
6. Ten Little Fish
7. Three Little Pigs

BONUS TRACKS:

8. Can You Name That Animal Sound?
9. Old MacDonald's Letter Farm
10. Bought Me A Cat
11. Five Little Skunks
12. The Animal Alphabet
13. Betty Bunny
14. The Rattlin Bog
15. The Green Grass Grew All Around
16. Be Kind To Your Web Footed Friends
17. How Much Wood?
18. Froggy, You're So Green
19. The Crawdad Song
20. The Old Gray Mare

FARMER GROVER HAS A FARM

Farmer Grover has a farm, **E-I-E-I-O**.
And on that farm he has three pigs, **E-I-E-I-O**.
With an oink-oink here and an oink-oink there.
Here an oink, there an oink, everywhere an oink-oink.
Farmer Grover has a farm, **E-I-E-I-O**.

oink-oink!
oink-oink!

Can you make the sound
of each of the animals
on Farmer Grover's Farm?

Farmer Grover has a farm, E-I-E-I-O.
And on this farm he has a sheep, E-I-E-I-O.
With a BAA-BAA here and a BAA-BAA there.
Here a BAA, there a BAA, everywhere a BAA-BAA.
Farmer Grover has a farm, E-I-E-I-O.

Farmer Grover has a farm, **E-I-E-I-O**.
And on this farm he has a cow, **E-I-E-I-O**
With a MOO-MOO here and a MOO-MOO there.
Here a MOO, there a MOO, everywhere a MOO-MOO.
Farmer Grover has a farm, **E-I-E-I-O**.

THE FARMER IN THE DELL

The farmer in the dell.
The farmer in the dell.
Hi-ho, the derry-o, the farmer in the dell.

The farmer takes a **DOG**.
The farmer takes a **DOG**.
Hi-ho, the derry-o, the farmer takes a **DOG**.

The dog takes a **CAT**.
The dog takes a **CAT**.
Hi-ho, the derry-o, the dog takes a **CAT**.

The cat takes a **RAT**.
The cat takes a **RAT**.
Hi-ho, the derry-o, the cat takes a **RAT**.

The rat takes the **CHEESE**.
The rat takes the **CHEESE**.
Hi-ho, the derry-o, the rat takes the **CHEESE**.

The **CHEESE** stands alone.
The **CHEESE** stands alone.
Hi-ho, the derry-o, the **CHEESE** stands alone.

SIX LITTLE DUCKS

SIX little ducks that I once knew,

Fat ones, skinny ones, fair ones too,

But the one little duck with the feather on his back,

He led the others with a **QUACK, QUACK, QUACK**!

QUACK, QUACK, QUACK! **QUACK, QUACK, QUACK**!

He led the others with a **QUACK, QUACK, QUACK**!

Down to the river they would go,

wibble-wobble, wibble-wobble, to and fro,

But the one little duck with the feather on his back,

He led the others with a **QUACK, QUACK, QUACK**!

QUACK, QUACK, QUACK! **QUACK, QUACK, QUACK**!

He led the others with a **QUACK, QUACK, QUACK**!

Home from the river they would come,
Wibble-wobble, wibble-wobble, ho-hum-hum,
But the one little duck with the feather on his back,
He led the others with a **QUACK**, **QUACK**, **QUACK**!
QUACK, **QUACK**, **QUACK**! **QUACK**, **QUACK**, **QUACK**!
He led the others with a **QUACK**, **QUACK**, **QUACK**!

Point to and count each duck!
What else can you count on the page?

1 2 3 4 5 6

A little **CAT**, cat, cat
Sat on a **MAT**, mat, mat
And wore a **HAT**, hat, hat
And liked to **CHAT**, chat, chat
And the little **CAT**, cat, cat
Was mighty **FAT**, fat, fat.
What do you think of **THAT**?

There was a **DOG**, dog, dog
Who liked a **FROG**, frog, frog
Down by the **BOG**, bog, bog
Up on a **LOG**, log, log.
Now that **DOG**, dog, dog
Would often **JOG**, jog, jog
To see his friend the **FROG**.

How many words can you
think of that rhyme with cat?

Miss Pretty **PIG**, pig, pig
Wore a **WIG**, wig, wig
While doing the **JIG**, jig, jig
Eating a **FIG**, fig, fig.
Now Pretty **PIG**, pig, pig
Said it's her **GIG**, gig, gig.
Can you really **DIG**?

Now little **CAT**, cat, cat
On the **MAT**, mat, mat
And the **DOG**, dog, dog
That liked the **FROG**, frog, frog
And Miss **PIG**, pig, pig
Who wore a **WIG**, wig, wig

It's a rhyming THING-A-MA-JIG,
Rhyming THING-A-MA-JIG.

There was a farmer had a dog
and BINGO was his name-o.

B-I-N-G-O, B-I-N-G-O, B-I-N-G-O,

and BINGO was his name-o.

When you see the 🐾 clap your hands instead of saying the letter.

There was a farmer had a dog
and BINGO was his name-o.

🐾-I-N-G-O, 🐾-I-N-G-O, 🐾-I-N-G-O,

and BINGO was his name-o.

There was a farmer had a dog
and BINGO was his name-o.

🐾-🐾-N-G-O, 🐾-🐾-N-G-O, 🐾-🐾-N-G-O,

and BINGO was his name-o.

There was a farmer had a dog and BINGO was his name-o.

🐾-🐾-🐾-G-O, 🐾-🐾-🐾-G-O,
🐾-🐾-🐾-G-O,
and BINGO was his name-o.

There was a farmer had a dog and BINGO was his name-o.

🐾-🐾-🐾-🐾-O, 🐾-🐾-🐾-🐾-O,
🐾-🐾-🐾-🐾-O,
and BINGO was his name-o.

There was a farmer had a dog and BINGO was his name-o.

🐾-🐾-🐾-🐾-🐾, 🐾-🐾-🐾-🐾-🐾,
🐾-🐾-🐾-🐾-🐾,
and BINGO was his name-o.

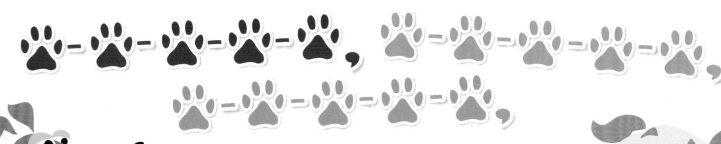

TEN little fish swam in a stream.
Red and blue and some were green.
They chased each other until one said...

"I am tired. I'm going to bed."

Can you count
backwards
from 10 to 1?

10 9 8 7 6 5 4 3 2 1

NINE little fish swam in a stream.
Red and blue and some were green.
They chased each other until one said,
"I am tired. I'm going to bed."

EIGHT little fish swam in a stream.
Red and blue and some were green.
They chased each other until one said,
"I am tired. I'm going to bed."

SEVEN little fish swam in a stream.
Red and blue and some were green.
They chased each other until one said,
"I am tired. I'm going to bed."

SIX little fish swam in a stream.
Red and blue and some were green.
They chased each other until one said,
"I am tired. I'm going to bed."

FIVE little fish swam in a stream.
Red and blue and some were green.
They chased each other until one said,
"I am tired. I'm going to bed."

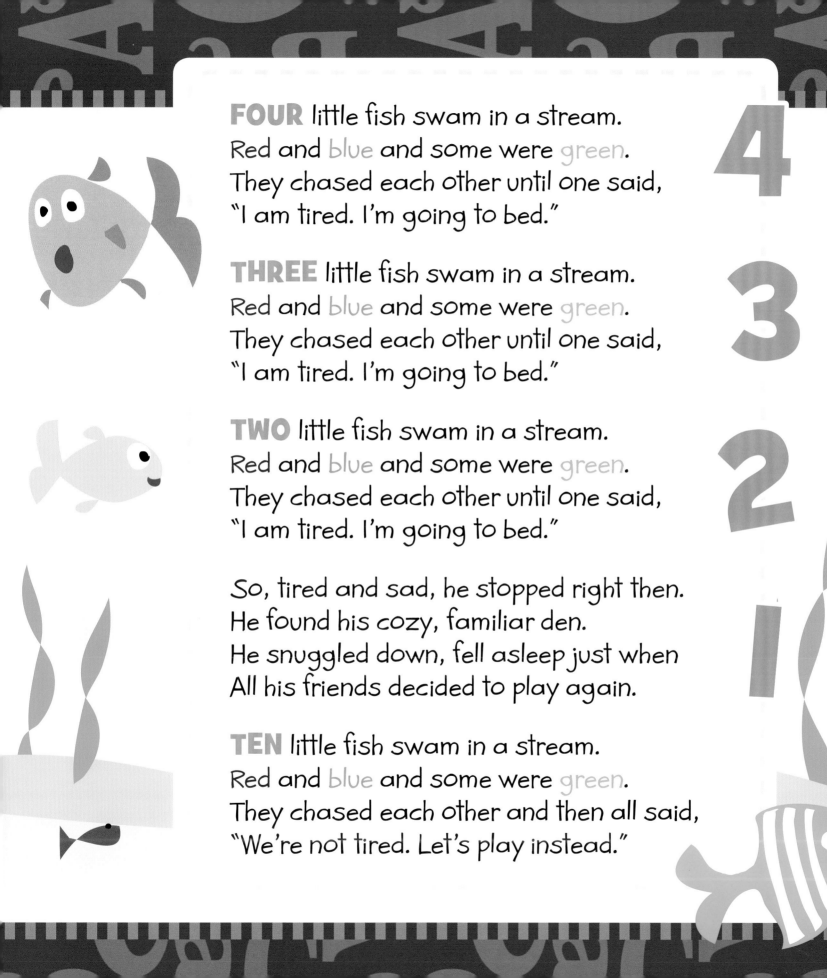

FOUR little fish swam in a stream.
Red and blue and some were green.
They chased each other until one said,
"I am tired. I'm going to bed."

THREE little fish swam in a stream.
Red and blue and some were green.
They chased each other until one said,
"I am tired. I'm going to bed."

TWO little fish swam in a stream.
Red and blue and some were green.
They chased each other until one said,
"I am tired. I'm going to bed."

So, tired and sad, he stopped right then.
He found his cozy, familiar den.
He snuggled down, fell asleep just when
All his friends decided to play again.

TEN little fish swam in a stream.
Red and blue and some were green.
They chased each other and then all said,
"We're not tired. Let's play instead."

THREE LITTLE PIGS

ONE little, **TWO** little, **THREE** little piggies,
ONE little, **TWO** little, **THREE** little piggies,
ONE little, **TWO** little, **THREE** little piggies,
Livin' on Farmer Grover's farm.

One little piggy just goes oink.
Two little piggies go oink oink.
Three little piggies go oink, oink, oink.
Livin' on Farmer Grover's farm.

ONE little, **TWO** little, **THREE** little piggies,
ONE little, **TWO** little, **THREE** little piggies,
ONE little, **TWO** little, **THREE** little piggies,
Livin' on Farmer Grover's farm.

oink

oink

oink